NATIONAL CURRICULUM LINKED

practise

TABLES

4×2=8 3×6=18 5×5=25 3×9=27

7×3=21

A

① $3 \times 3 =$ ☐

② $2 \times 5 =$ ☐

③ $6 \times 4 =$ ☐

④ $9 \times 2 =$ ☐

⑤ $8 \times 3 =$ ☐

⑥ $5 \times 0 =$ ☐

⑦
$$\begin{array}{r} 7 \\ \times 2 \\ \hline \end{array}$$

⑧
$$\begin{array}{r} 5 \\ \times 4 \\ \hline \end{array}$$

⑨
$$\begin{array}{r} 4 \\ \times 0 \\ \hline \end{array}$$

⑩
$$\begin{array}{r} 6 \\ \times 3 \\ \hline \end{array}$$

B

① $4 \div 2 =$ ☐

② $10 \div 5 =$ ☐

③ $12 \div 3 =$ ☐

④ $16 \div 4 =$ ☐

⑤ $12 \div 2 =$ ☐

⑥ $15 \div 3 =$ ☐

⑦ $3 \overline{)\ 9\ }$

⑧ $5 \overline{)25}$

⑨ $2 \overline{)14}$

⑩ $4 \overline{)16}$

5×3

6×2

4×2

Draw arrows to the correct answers.

①

× 2

4	6
6	12
3	8

②

× 3

9	12
4	27
0	0

③

× 5

4	40
9	20
8	45

④

× 4

7	28
3	16
4	12

Fill in the answers.

⑤

× 2

5

7

3

⑥

× 3

6

8

7

2

You can play this game alone or with a friend.

You need a dice and different coloured counters for each person.

Rules

① Throw the dice. Multiply the score by **3** and cover the answer with your colour counter.

② Next player's turn.

③ Keep playing until all the numbers are covered.

The person who covers the most numbers wins the game.

6

18   3

12   15   9

3   6   12   9

18   6   12   9   3

Fruit shop

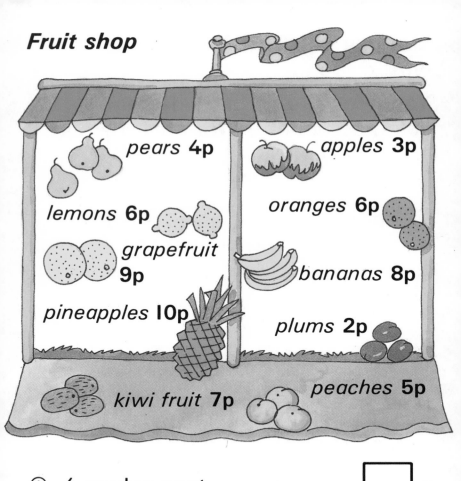

pears **4p**

apples **3p**

lemons **6p**

oranges **6p**

grapefruit **9p**

bananas **8p**

pineapples **10p**

plums **2p**

kiwi fruit **7p**

peaches **5p**

① 4 apples cost . . . . ☐ p

② 4 oranges cost . . . . ☐ p

③ 2 bananas cost . . . . ☐ p

④ 5 plums cost . . . . ☐ p

⑤ 7 peaches cost . . . . ☐ p

⑥ 6 pears cost . . . . ☐ p

⑦ 9 lemons cost . . . . ☐ p

⑧ 3 grapefruit cost . . . . ☐ p

⑨ 6 pineapples cost . . . . ☐ p

⑩ 7 kiwi fruit cost . . . . ☐ p

4

Missing numbers

① $4 \times 4 = \boxed{}$

② $6 \times \boxed{} = 12$

③ $5 \times \boxed{} = 15$

④ $\boxed{} \times 3 = 9$

⑤ $\boxed{} \times 2 = 14$

⑥ $4 \times \boxed{} = 20$

⑦ $9 \times \boxed{} = 18$

⑧ $\boxed{} \times 4 = 0$

⑨ $8 \times \boxed{} = 24$

⑩ $\boxed{} \times 5 = 25$

⑪
$$\begin{array}{r} 8 \\ \times\ \boxed{} \\ \hline 32 \\ \hline \end{array}$$

⑫
$$\begin{array}{r} 9 \\ \times\ \boxed{} \\ \hline 45 \\ \hline \end{array}$$

⑬
$$\begin{array}{r} \boxed{} \\ \times\ 3 \\ \hline 21 \\ \hline \end{array}$$

⑭
$$\begin{array}{r} 0 \\ \times\ 5 \\ \hline \boxed{} \\ \hline \end{array}$$

5

How much do the toy farm animals cost?

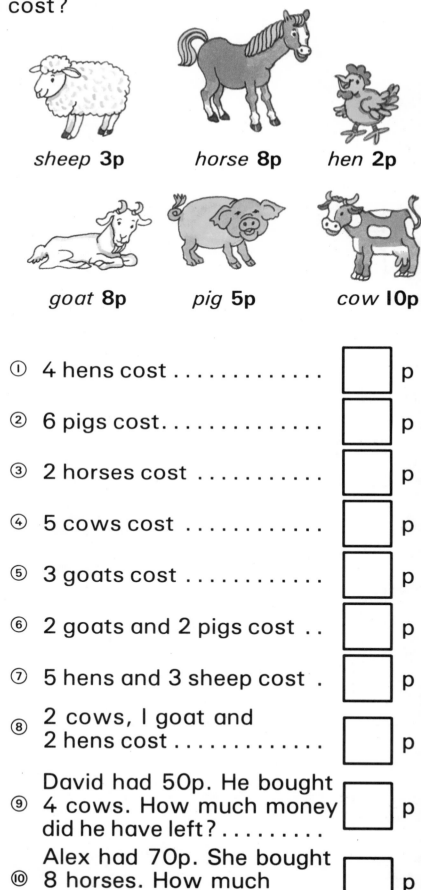

sheep **3p**   horse **8p**   hen **2p**

goat **8p**   pig **5p**   cow **10p**

① 4 hens cost . . . . [ ] p

② 6 pigs cost. . . . . [ ] p

③ 2 horses cost . . . . [ ] p

④ 5 cows cost . . . . [ ] p

⑤ 3 goats cost . . . . [ ] p

⑥ 2 goats and 2 pigs cost .. [ ] p

⑦ 5 hens and 3 sheep cost . [ ] p

⑧ 2 cows, I goat and 2 hens cost . . . . [ ] p

⑨ David had 50p. He bought 4 cows. How much money did he have left? . . . . [ ] p

⑩ Alex had 70p. She bought 8 horses. How much money did she have left? [ ] p

6

A

① $7 \times 6 = \boxed{}$

② $9 \times 8 = \boxed{}$

③ $7 \times 9 = \boxed{}$

④ $6 \times 7 = \boxed{}$

⑤ $9 \times 6 = \boxed{}$

⑥ $8 \times 8 = \boxed{}$

⑦
$$\begin{array}{r} 6 \\ \times\, 9 \\ \hline \end{array}$$

⑧
$$\begin{array}{r} 9 \\ \times\, 9 \\ \hline \end{array}$$

⑨
$$\begin{array}{r} 4 \\ \times\, 7 \\ \hline \end{array}$$

⑩
$$\begin{array}{r} 9 \\ \times\, 7 \\ \hline \end{array}$$

B

① $36 \div 9 = \boxed{}$

② $42 \div 6 = \boxed{}$

③ $81 \div 9 = \boxed{}$

④ $63 \div 7 = \boxed{}$

⑤ $90 \div 9 = \boxed{}$

⑥ $72 \div 8 = \boxed{}$

⑦ $6\overline{)36}$

⑧ $7\overline{)42}$

⑨ $9\overline{)54}$

⑩ $8\overline{)64}$

Making multiplication sums

① 8 ladybirds.
Each ladybird has 6 legs.
How many legs altogether?

$$\boxed{8} \times \boxed{6} = \boxed{}$$

② 5 octopuses.
Each octopus has 8 legs.
How many legs altogether?

$$\boxed{} \times \boxed{} = \boxed{}$$

③ 4 children.
Each child has 10 toes.
How many toes altogether?

$$\boxed{} \times \boxed{} = \boxed{}$$

④ 7 spiders.
Each spider has 8 legs.
How many legs altogether?

$$\boxed{} \times \boxed{} = \boxed{}$$

⑤ 3 tricycles.
3 wheels on each tricycle.
How many wheels altogether?

$$\boxed{} \times \boxed{} = \boxed{}$$

⑥ 6 flower pots.
4 flowers in each pot.
How many flowers altogether?

$$\boxed{} \times \boxed{} = \boxed{}$$

Missing numbers

① ☐ × 9 = 81

② 4 × ☐ = 32

③ 9 × 6 = ☐

④ 7 × ☐ = 35

⑤ 8 × ☐ = 48

⑥ ☐ × 9 = 36

⑦ ☐ × 10 = 70

⑧ 5 × 9 = ☐

⑨ 9 × ☐ = 72

⑩ 7 × ☐ = 42

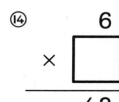

⑪
```
    7
×  ☐
─────
   49
```

⑫
```
   10
×   8
─────
   ☐
```

⑬
```
    8
×  ☐
─────
   64
```

⑭
```
    6
×  ☐
─────
   42
```

9

Targets

Multiply by the bullseye and fill in the missing numbers to complete the targets.

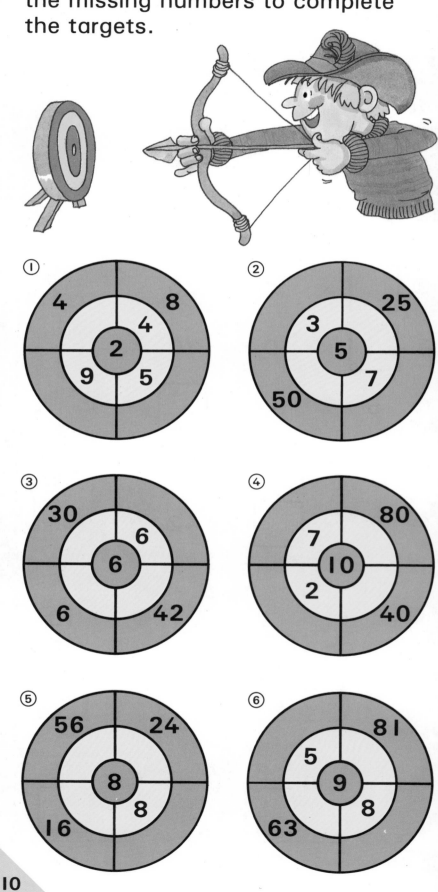

Sharing

A How many 9s? ☐

How many 6s? ☐

How many 3s? ☐

18 cars

How many 2s? ☐

B How many 8s? ☐

How many 6s? ☐

24 balloons

How many 4s? ☐

How many 3s? ☐

16 marbles

C How many 8s? ☐

How many 4s? ☐

D How many 9s? ☐

How many 3s? ☐

27 dominoes

E How many 10s? ☐

How many 6s? ☐

30 puzzles

How many 5s? ☐

Remainders

Each of these division sums has
a **remainder**. eg **29 ÷ 4 = 7 rem 1**

①   5 ÷ 2 = _____

②   7 ÷ 3 = _____

③   9 ÷ 4 = _____

④   8 ÷ 3 = _____

⑤   11 ÷ 4 = _____

⑥   15 ÷ 2 = _____

⑦   51 ÷ 6 = _____

⑧   14 ÷ 9 = _____

⑨   29 ÷ 8 = _____

⑩   67 ÷ 9 = _____

⑪   42 ÷ 8 = _____

⑫   69 ÷ 7 = _____

Number families

①
$2 \times 3 = \boxed{}$

$3 \times 2 = \boxed{}$

$6 \div 3 = \boxed{}$

$6 \div 2 = \boxed{}$

②
$5 \times 2 = \boxed{}$

$2 \times 5 = \boxed{}$

$10 \div 2 = \boxed{}$

$10 \div 5 = \boxed{}$

③
$4 \times 5 = \boxed{}$

$5 \times 4 = \boxed{}$

$20 \div 5 = \boxed{}$

$20 \div 4 = \boxed{}$

④ Make up your own families using these numbers.

$\boxed{3}$ $\boxed{4}$ $\boxed{12}$

_____   _____

_____   _____

⑤ $\boxed{7}$ $\boxed{8}$ $\boxed{56}$

_____   _____

_____   _____

13

Problems

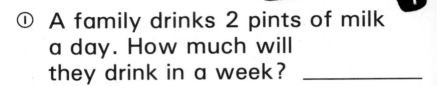

① A family drinks 2 pints of milk a day. How much will they drink in a week? _____

② There were 5 nests with 6 eggs in each nest. How many eggs altogether? _____

③ How much would 7 pencils cost if each one costs 9p? _____

④ There were 4 bowls with 6 goldfish in each bowl. How many fish altogether? _____

⑤ If Adam watches television for 3 hours every day, how many hours will he watch in one week? _____

⑥ If a school table seats 8 children, how many tables will you need for 40 children? _____

⑦ Share 24 oranges equally into 3 boxes. How many oranges are there in each box? _____

Connect four numbers

This is a multiplication game for 2 players. You will need 2 different coloured sets of counters and a calculator to check your answers.

You can only use these numbers:

0	1	2	3	4	5	6	7	8

Take it in turns to multiply two of the above numbers together.

Place your counter on the answer number below.

The first player with four counters in a row wins. The line of four can be across, down or diagonal.

16	28	8	4	5
35	7	32	48	40
21	56	6	10	18
20	15	12	0	3
14	42	24	30	2

Complete this multiplication table.

×	1	2	3	4	5	6	7	8	9	10
1										
2										
3										
4										
5										
6										
7										
8										
9										
10										

Quick test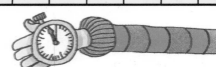

You have *1 minute* to answer these.

①   6 × 2 = _____

②   3 × 7 = _____

③   4 × 3 = _____

④   5 × 6 = _____

⑤   9 × 0 = _____

⑥   8 × 4 = _____

⑦   9 × 8 = _____

⑧   10 × 6 = _____

⑨   4 × 7 = _____

⑩   10 ×10 = _____

16